Maze Quest

ILLUSTRATED BY
LAURA HORTON
STORY BY
WILLIAM POTTER

ARCTURUS

HOW TO USE THIS BOOK

Most mazes in this book have more than one exit. When you reach the edge of a page, follow the instructions, turning to the page number indicated.

Sometimes your path will be blocked by obstacles or enemies. Go back and find a new route!

The start point to a maze is always indicated by Jada and Tim.

CRYSTAL FOREST

Cobble leads Jada and Tim into a sparkling forest, where crystalline creatures gambol among giant gems. See what you can find on your path through the glittering trees.

Wow! That huge shield fit into this magic pouch.

Watch where you step! Everything is made of crystal here, even the animals!

Collect the Sun Gem.

To the Valley of Wisps (page 10)

CAN YOU FIND ...

2   3   3

To the Shifting Swamp (page 6)

If you have the Eternal Flame, turn to page 12.

You will need to collect certain items by passing over them. You can make a record of the items you have collected in the checklist on page 3.

To complete the story, you must travel from page to page until you reach Amaza's Palace. You will need every item on the checklist to defeat her!

Some routes and exits are blocked unless you have the right item listed under your treasures. You may have to pass through some mazes twice to finish the book.

INTO THE MAZE

When Jada told her friend Tim she wanted to explore the Forgotten Forest, he pulled a face. "I'm just getting to a good bit in my adventure story!" Little did they realize that their walk in the woods would be the beginning of an incredible quest ...

Pinned to the tree next to the door is a piece of parchment that looks like a checklist. What can it be for?

THORNWOOD

Jada and Tim step through the round door … and it slams shut behind them! They find themselves in a strange wood, with no way back. Can you help them to find another way out, keeping clear of the thorns?

SHIFTING SWAMP

With their clothes torn by thorns, Jada and Tim put on the outfits they found in the wood and follow Cobble's lead through a swamp full of spooky creatures. Can you see a safe path?

Can you tell us where we are? How will we get home?

Why, you're in the Hinter Realms! This kingdom is ruled by cruel Queen Amaza, whose enchantment has turned every field and forest into a mysterious maze.

If you want to leave this place, you must break the spell!

To Thornwood (page 4)

To the Crystal
Forest (page 8)

Collect the Ancient Shield

CAN YOU FIND ...

~~3~~ ~~1~~ 6

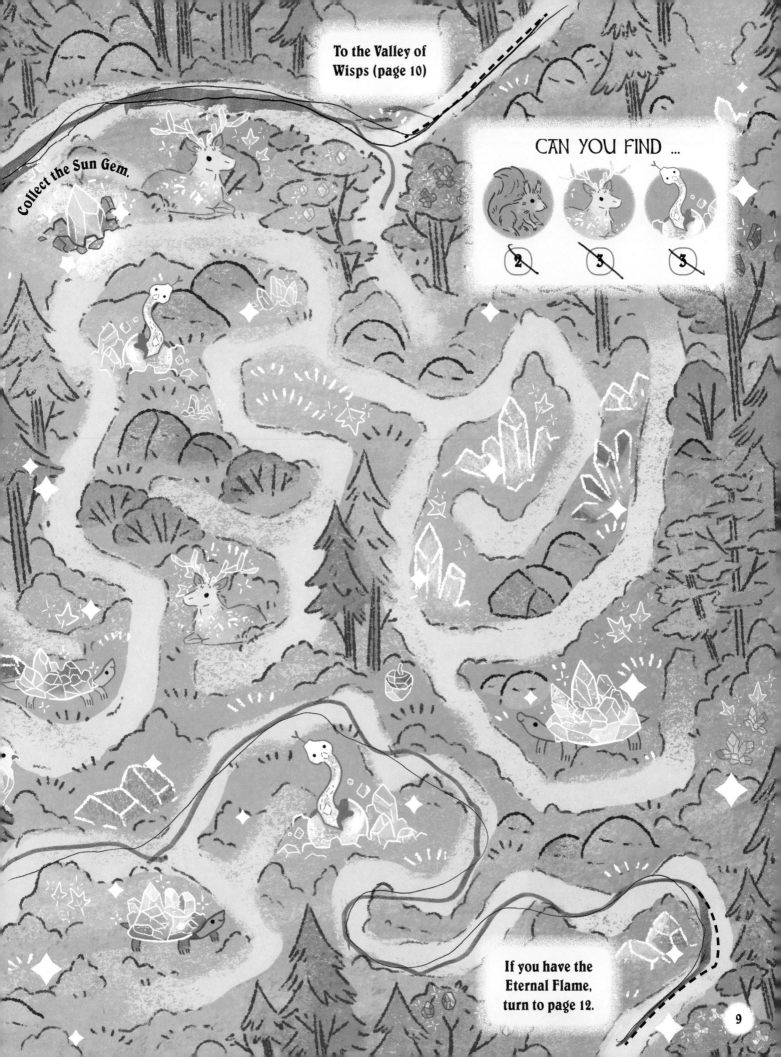

To the Valley of
Wisps (page 10)

Collect the Sun Gem.

CAN YOU FIND ...

2 3 3

If you have the
Eternal Flame,
turn to page 12.

9

VALLEY OF WISPS

Next, the trio arrive in a crumbling, forgotten town patrolled by ghostly creatures made of memories. Lead them through the maze and listen to Sage, the wise old wizard.

10

To the Shifting Swamp (page 6)

Collect the Eternal Flame.

CAN YOU FIND ...

4

4

7

To the Crystal Forest (page 8)

11

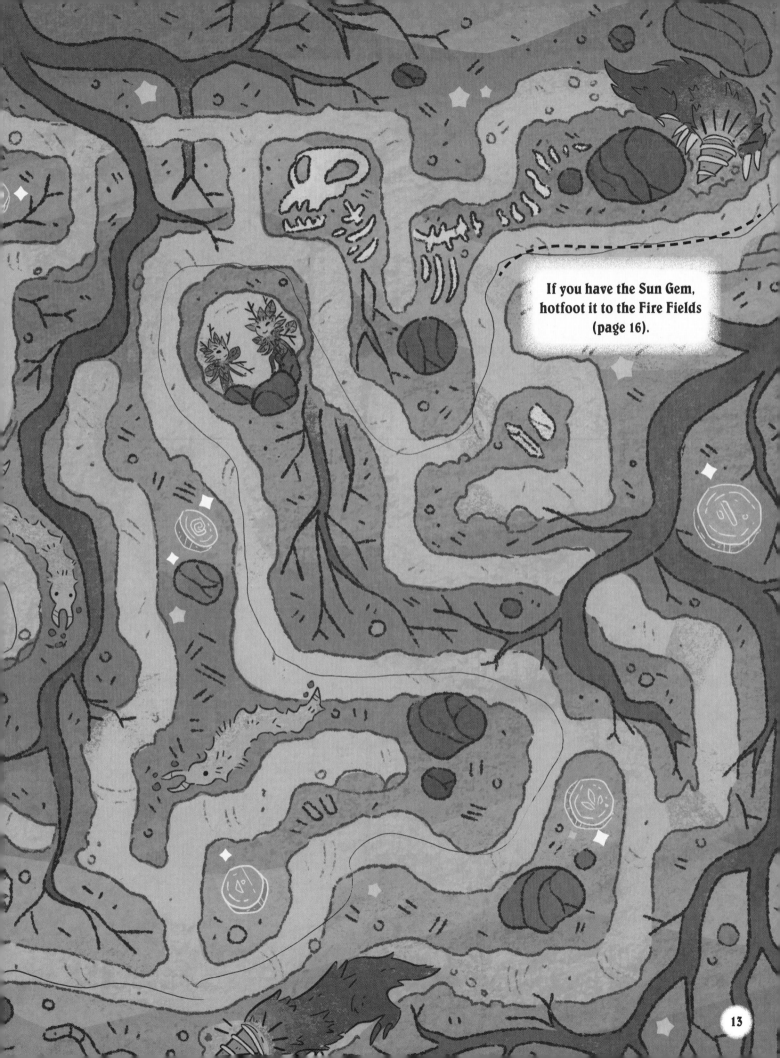

If you have the Sun Gem, hotfoot it to the Fire Fields (page 16).

LIGHTNING LAND

Look out! These lightning-wielding lords and ladies are clashing over ancient treasures. Dash through the danger zone!

Collect the Singing Sword.

Careful not to be hit by lightning!

How do we do that?

By being lucky!

CAN YOU FIND ...

3   5   7

To the Fire Fields
(page 16)

To the Burrows
(page 12)

FIRE FIELDS

Jada, Tim, and Cobble arrive in a land of red-hot rocks and lava. The Sun Gem will shield them from the heat ... but it can't protect them from Amaza's champion, the Night Knight!

It's so hot here my shoes are melting!

CAN YOU FIND ...

1   3   5

GINGERBREAD TOWN

Our intrepid adventurers are glad to be back on solid ground. This whole town is made of candy, cake, and chocolate. Don't bump into anyone on your way!

CAN YOU FIND ...

4

4

5

This looks friendlier! Can we stay here a while?

No, we need to press on the palace!

To the Sparkling City (page 30)

To Bounceberg (page 28)

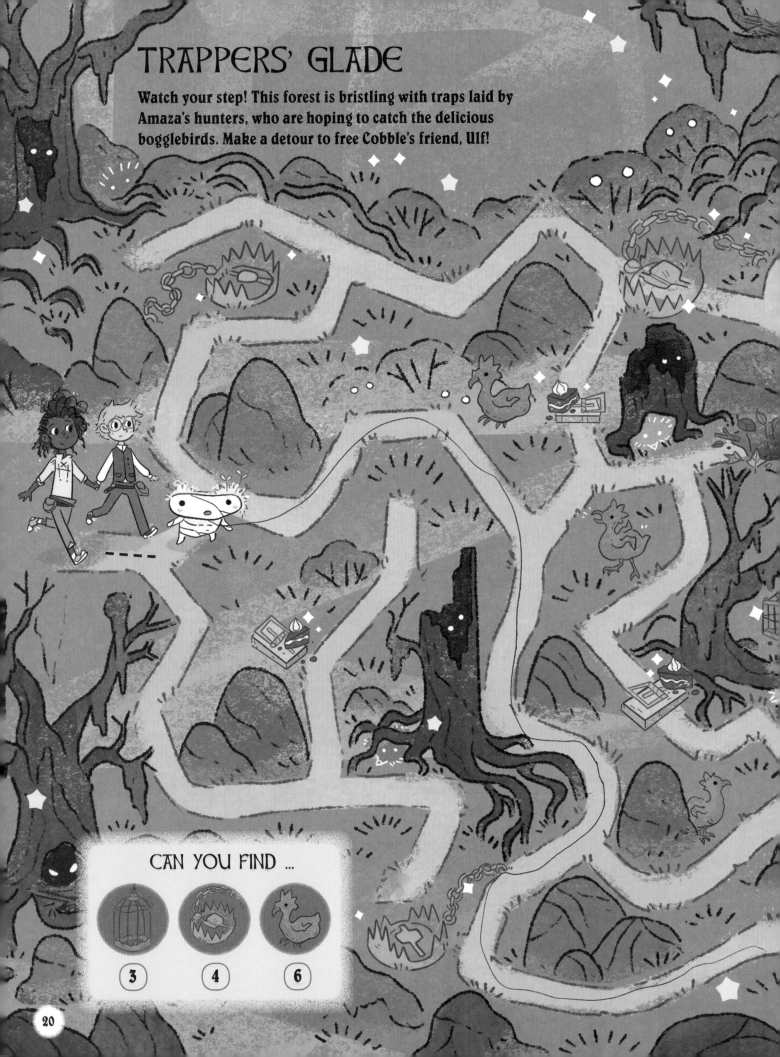

TRAPPERS' GLADE

Watch your step! This forest is bristling with traps laid by Amaza's hunters, who are hoping to catch the delicious bogglebirds. Make a detour to free Cobble's friend, Ulf!

CAN YOU FIND ...

3   4   6

If you have the Climbing Gear, clamber to page 22.

Collect the Climbing Gear.

To the Fire Fields (page 16)

Untangle me from this rope and I'll help show you a way out.

TOWER TREE

The rope and climbing gear the friends collected comes in handy right away—the next path is up a giant tree. Can you trace it?

To the Eyrie (page 24)

CAN YOU FIND ...

3

4

5

To Trappers' Glade (page 20)

23

THE EYRIE

At the top of the tree, the trio discover a flock of ratbats. You can tiptoe through their nests, but don't touch the creatures!

CAN YOU FIND ...

1   4   7

To the Sky
Kingdom
(page 26)

Collect the Chainmail Shirt.

SKY KINGDOM

Some feathered friends offer Jada, Tim, and Cobble a ride. But beware—the clouds are not as fluffy as they first look.

Jump aboard a goldgull and steer it around the clouds.

Hold on tight, everyone!

CAN YOU FIND ...

4   5   6

To Gingerbread
Town (page 18)

BOUNCEBERG

This town is on the side of a cliff, and everyone has a spring in their step—literally! Dodge the townsfolk, who are bouncing from place to place, and beware Queen Amaza's sinister Spymaster. Quick, hop to it!

The purple pixies are my spies. They have been tracking your every move. Have you spotted them on other pages?

These springy shoes will help us get the jump on Amaza!

To Gingerbread Town (page 18)

CAN YOU FIND ...

3   4   6

If you have the
River Raft, splash
over to page 32.

To Gingerbread Town (page 18)

Collect the River Raft.

To Bounceberg (page 28)

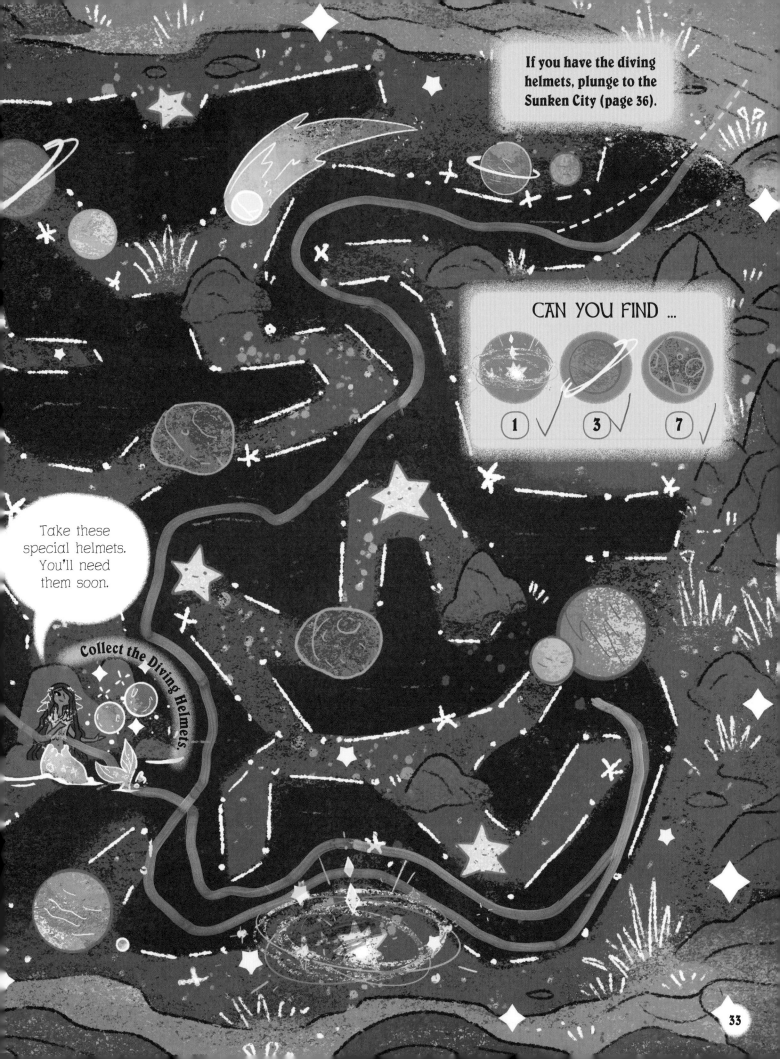

If you have the diving helmets, plunge to the Sunken City (page 36).

CAN YOU FIND ...

1 ✓   3 ✓   7 ✓

Take these special helmets. You'll need them soon.

Collect the Diving Helmets.

HUNGRY JUNGLE

The trio arrive in a wild jungle filled with sharp-toothed flowers. Can they get through without ending up as plant food? And look out—the Night Knight's back!

These plants are carnivorous. Try not to get added to the menu!

To the Sunken City (page 36)

SUNKEN CITY

Jada and Tim will need to wear their diving helmets to swim through this underwater kingdom.

It's just as well that I don't need a helmet!

To the Cosmic Pool (page 32)

To the Catacombs
(page 38)

Collect the Sea
Queen's Trident.

To the Hungry
Jungle (page 34)

CAN YOU FIND ...

3 4 5

CATACOMBS

Still soggy from their their swim, the trio enter a dark cave system that is home to countless cats. Keep up the pace—this is no time for a catnap!

Cute! A cave of kittens!

Take care! They have sharp claws!

Collect the Invisibility Cloak.

CAN YOU FIND ...

1   3   4

To the Hungry Jungle (page 34)

To the Sunken City (page 36)

MOODY MOUNTAIN

The three heroes have a hard and slippery climb ahead, with the extra danger of ice traps and angry snowbeasts. Help them find a safe path!

If you have the River Raft, turn to page 42.

CAN YOU FIND ...

6

6

3

40

To the Thirsty Desert (page 44)

41

SHIMMERING STREAMS

Over the ridge, the ice has turned into meltwater. It's time for some whitewater rafting ... but keep an eye out for the snapping fish and evil ducks!

CAN YOU FIND ...

5   5   6

To the Crags
(page 52)

THIRSTY DESERT

The friends step onto golden sands. What a dry, arid place!
Only the long-tongued aquadillos can sense the secret
springs beneath the surface.

We'd better
hurry through here
or we'll pass out
from thirst!

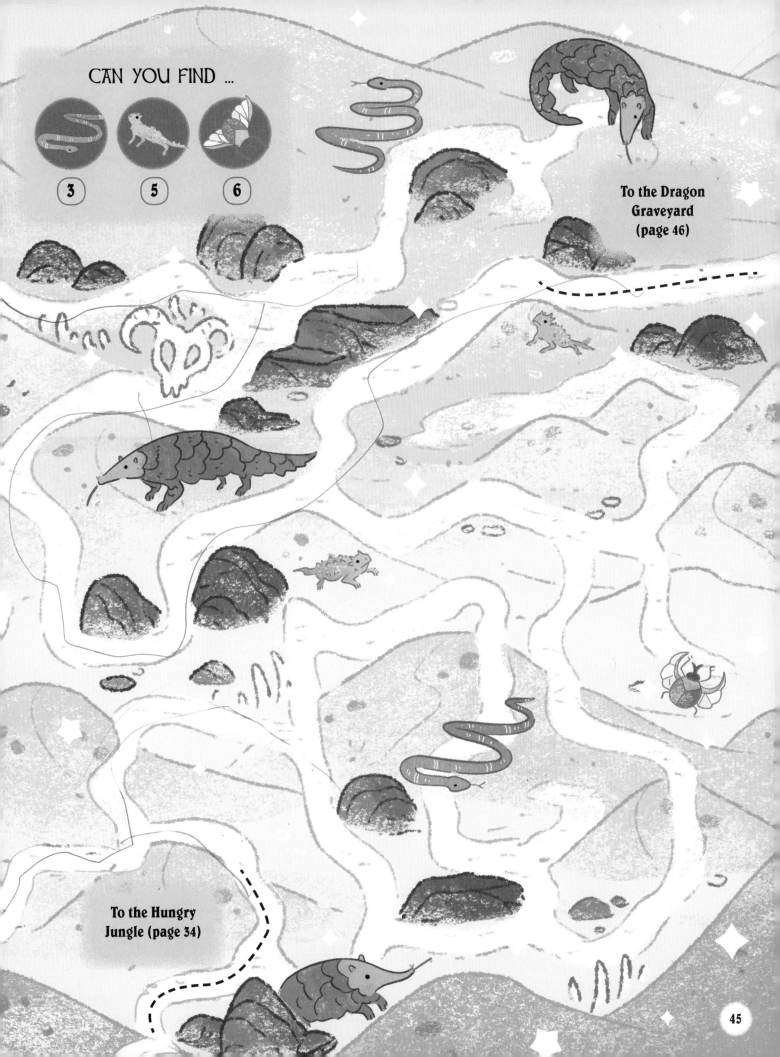

CAN YOU FIND ...

3   5   6

To the Dragon
Graveyard
(page 46)

To the Hungry
Jungle (page 34)

DRAGON GRAVEYARD

Next, the tired trio arrive at the graveyard of extinct battlebeasts. Is there a path through all the ancient bones?

To Bubbleborough
(page 48)

To the Thirsty
Desert (page 44)

BUBBLEBOROUGH

The three heroes find themselves in a floating garden populated by living balloon animals.

Step carefully here—you don't want to burst anyone!

Collect the Golden Gauntlet.

To the Dragon Graveyard (page 46)

CAN YOU FIND ...

1   1   1

To the Crags
(page 52)

To Bug Bridges
(page 50)

To the Shimmering
Streams (page 42)

To Bubbleborough
(page 48)

Collect the Winged Helmet

53

GOOP LAND

The trio arrive in a goopy land of slippery slime trails and slitherbeasts. And look—it's Amaza's patrol!

To Bug Bridges
(page 50)

Try not to slip over!

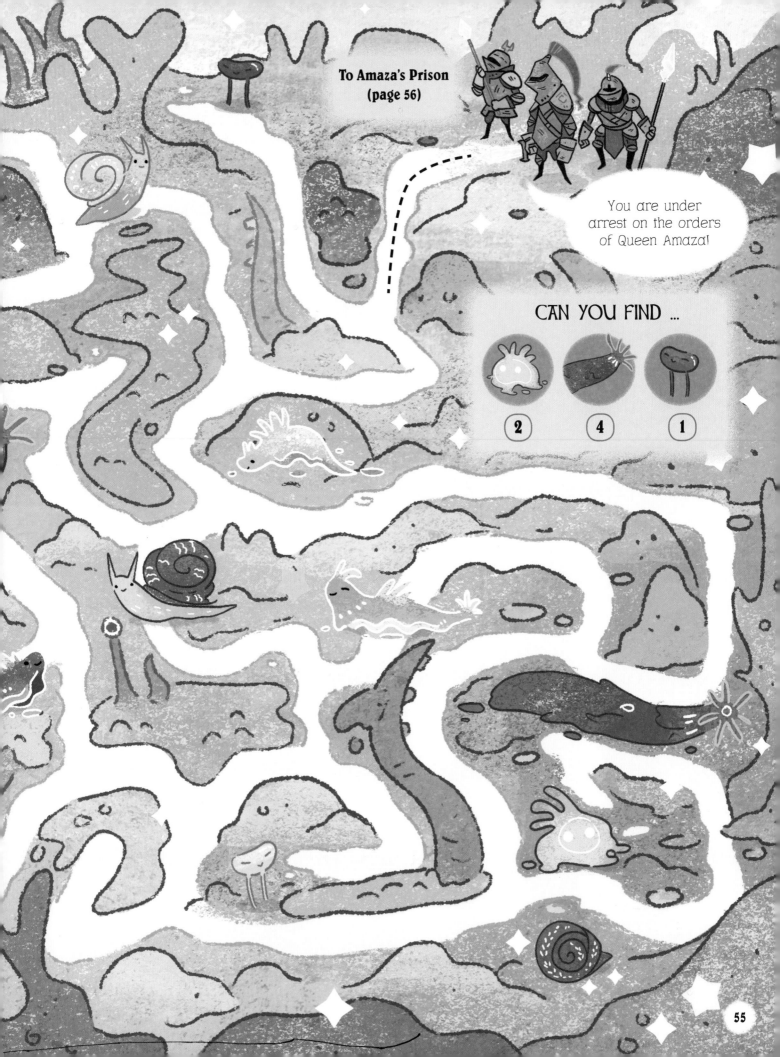

**To Amaza's Prison
(page 56)**

ANSWERS

Pages 4-5: Thornwood

Pages 6-7: Shifting Swamp

Pages 8-9: Crystal Forest

Pages 10-11: Valley of Wisps

Pages 12-13: The Burrows

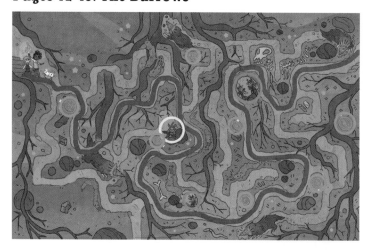

Pages 14-15: Lightning Land

Pages 16-17: Fire Fields

Pages 18-19: Gingerbread Town

Pages 20-21: Trappers' Glade

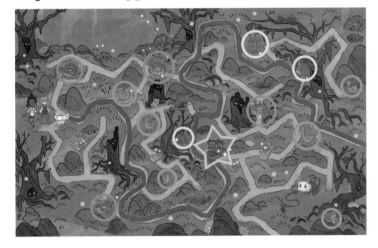

Pages 22-23: Tower Tree

Pages 24-25: The Eyrie

Pages 26-27: Sky Kingdom

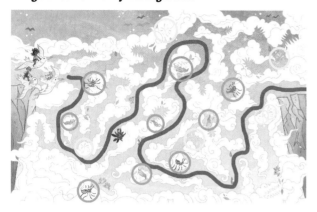

Pages 28-29: Bounceberg

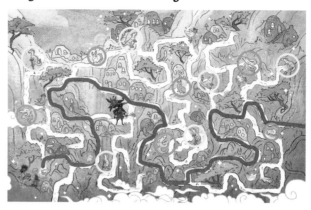

Pages 30-31: Sparkling City

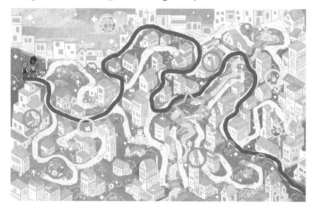

Pages 32-33: Cosmic Pool

Pages 34-35: Hungry Jungle

Pages 36-37: Sunken City

Pages 38-39: The Catacombs

Pages 40-41: Moody Mountain

Pages 42-43: Shimmering Streams

Pages 44-45: Thirsty Desert

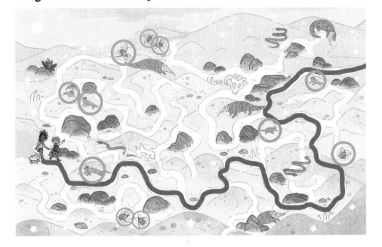

Pages 46-47: Dragon Graveyard

Pages 48-49: Bubbleborough

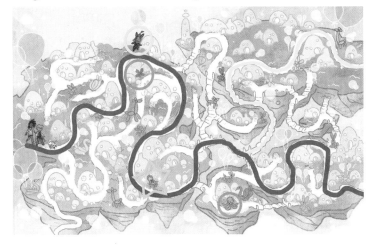

Pages 50-51: Bug Bridges

Pages 52-53: The Crags

Pages 54-55: Goop Land

Pages 56-57: Amaza's Prison

Pages 58-59: Amaza's Palace

ARCTURUS

This edition published in 2021 by Arcturus Publishing Limited
26/27 Bickels Yard, 151-153 Bermondsey Street,
London SE1 3HA

Author: William Potter
Illustrator: Laura Horton
Editor: Joe Harris
Designer: Sarah Fountain

ISBN: 978-1-3988-1197-3
CH008189NT
Supplier 29, Date 0821, Print run 11776

Printed in China

Page-by-Page Solution

**This is the quickest way for Jada and Tim to complete
their quest, but many other routes are possible.**

4-5 Thornwood (collect Quest Clothes) ➔ 6-7 Shifting
Swamp (collect Ancient Shield) ➔ 8-9 Crystal Forest
(collect Sun Gem) ➔ 10-11 Valley of Wisps (collect Eternal
Flame) ➔ 8-9 Crystal Forest again ➔ Use Eternal Flame
to access 12-13 The Burrows ➔ Use Sun Gem to access
16-17 Fire Fields ➔ 14-15 Lightning Land (collect Singing
Sword) ➔ 16-17 Fire Fields again ➔ Use Singing Sword
to access 20-21 Trappers' Glade (collect Climbing Gear)
➔ Use Climbing Gear to access 22-23 Tower Tree ➔
24-25 The Eyrie (collect Chainmail Shirt) ➔ 26-27 Sky
Kingdom ➔ 18-19 Gingerbread Town ➔ 30-31 Sparkling
City (collect River Raft) ➔ 28-29 Bounceberg ➔ Use
River Raft to access 32-33 Cosmic Pool (collect Diving
Helmets) ➔ Use Diving Helmets to access 36-37 Sunken
City (collect Sea Queen's Trident) ➔ 38-39 Catacombs
(collect Invisibility Cloak) ➔ 34-35 Hungry Jungle ➔
44-45 Thirsty Desert ➔ 46-47 Dragon Graveyard (collect
Eagle-Eye Bow) ➔ Back to 34-35 Hungry Jungle ➔ Use
Sea Queen's Trident to access 40-41 Moody Mountain
➔ Use River Raft to access 42-43 Shimmering Streams
➔ 52-53 The Crags (collect Winged Helmet) ➔ 48-49
Bubbleborough (collect Golden Gauntlet) ➔ 50-51 Bug
Bridges ➔ Use Invisibility Cloak to access 54-55 Goop
Land ➔ 56-57 Amaza's Prison ➔ 58-59 Amaza's Palace
➔ THE END